JOURNAL JUICE

Topics for Journal Writing, Drawing,
Dreaming, and Doodling

RENEE MATT

JOURNAL JUICE
Everyday Life Topics for Journal Writing,
Drawing, Dreaming and Doodling

ISBN: 978-1-7340059-0-5

Written and illustrated (including cover design) by Renee Matt

The contents of this book promotes the power of art therapy as an effective means of dealing with sometimes very difficult emotions. The author does not claim to be an authority in mental health; information and viewpoints contained in this book do not take the place of a mental health professional. Consult a professional for expert advice.

The author gratefully acknowledges the creators of the following licensed and freeware typefaces used in the cover art of this book:
'Against Myself,' 'Jenna Sue Pro,' and 'The Unseen'.

Printed in the United States of America.
First print edition 2019.

Published by Cavvy Ott, LLC
P.O. Box 225
Clermont, Iowa 52135

Mattie-Moon.com | 100-Passions.com

DEDICATION

To the amazing, kind souls who have left a lasting
impression on my life and who are now with me in spirit only.

To my family, who sees me as an artist. It has made me feel special
and given me the determination to make it to the finish line.

In the corridors of your
mind is a place of HONOR
for exceptional persons
who have shown KINDNESS,
INTEGRITY, and great
CHARACTER. When in doubt
and indecision, travel through
these hallways, and spend time
with those individuals who
INSPIRE and continue
to GUIDE you. -R. Matt

Your journey
begins
HERE...
DARE to make your
1st mark

CONTENTS

Introduction

Call it what you want: a journal, a diary, a guidebook. I invite you to linger and explore , maybe even scribble with wild abandon. It's a place to spend time with your thoughts and give them the credit they deserve. If it's the first time you've tried a book like this, have fun with it, it's yours to use in whatever form you can imagine.

I started by choosing topics I wanted to dive deeper into and started researching them.   The new insights naturally flowed out of my pen and into my drawings, giving me great personal satisfaction. Think of my artwork as a springboard for your own self-reflection. You might even find yourself inspired to draw a doodle or two, or color the pages instead, as another useful method to relax and reduce stress.

On a deeper level, art can help you heal mentally, physically, or spiritually. Through the creative process, people have an opportunity to deal with emotions, improve self-esteem and self-awareness, and decrease stress and anxiety.

Enjoy your journey of self-exploration as you grow in self-worth and confidence!

CHAPTER 1
Choose Happiness

What makes our heart sing is being in a healthy emotional state. Everything which makes us special and unique has a chance to flourish and grow. Think of all the simple things that bring you peace, get you excited, make your brain happy. This is where life gets good...

Happiness

4

Draw • Write • Get it onto Paper

5

YOU ARE SPECIAL

Just because my path is DIFFERENT doesn't mean I'm Lost

There is a crack in everything, that's how the LIGHT gets in
—LEONARD COHEN

NO ONE IS YOU—THAT IS YOUR POWER, YOU ARE A UNIQUE BEAUTIFUL SOUL

Let people be INSPIRED by YOUR Imperfections

The only thing you have that no one else has is you. your VOICE your MIND your STORY, your VISION. So write+draw+build +play+dance +LIVE only as YOU can.
—NEIL GAIMAN

Smiling releases endorphins (not dolphins)

WHAT SOAP IS TO THE BODY, LAUGHTER IS TO THE SOUL
— YIDDISH PROVERB

STRESS limits + NARROWS our attention, SMILING ☺ opens us up to multi-tasking and NEW INSIGHTS

Smiling EVERY DAY → trains your brain for Happiness

Each time you SMILE, it's a little Feel Good PARTY in your BRAIN!

LAUGHTER
BOOSTS IMMUNITY
IMPROVES MOOD
DECREASES STRESS + ANXIETY
EXPANDS THE LUNGS
AB WORK-OUT
RELEASES BOTTLED UP EMOTIONS
LET'S YOU LET GO of Defensiveness

SMILING MAKES YOU MORE CREATIVE

SMILING
• makes you look attractive, younger
• makes you feel more comfortable
• natural pain killer, elevates mood
• increases productivity
• evokes trustworthiness + confidence

Your creativity is revealed in many ways — parenting, relationships, wardrobe, problem solving, ideas, cooking, music, style!

EVERY DAY make MAGICAL *

CREATIVITY balances the BODY · HEART · MIND · SPIRIT

We all have a need for CREATIVITY and LIFE Experiences that fulfill us

ALWAYS HAVE A CREATIVE OUTLET!

The EBB and FLOW — OF — PASSION

EVERY DAY feed your Creativity

NO JOY

We find ourselves NOT GOOD AT OR NOT CARING about our JOB

EVERYTHING BECOMES A STRUGGLE when out of Alignment with our Creative Expression

IT DOESN'T MATTER HOW MANY YEARS or DECADES you've poured into something — LET IT GO DON'T HOLD ONTO IT if it doesn't flow easily, you're wasting time meant for BETTER THINGS

Ahhhh!

WELCOME to pure Joy

Creativity Boosts HAPPINESS!

INCREDIBLE!

WONDERFUL!

HAPPY HAPPY HAPPY

EFFORTLESS!

Imagine...

Everyone is Capable of Creativity EVERYDAY is energy

You are Resourceful! • INGENIOUS! • BRILLIANT!

the state of creative expression

WHEN YOU SPEND A LOT OF TIME IN CREATIVE EXPRESSION, YOU WILL FIND YOUR LIFE BEGIN TO WORK... IT FEELS EFFORTLESS... NOT A STRUGGLE. ~Steve Pavlina

ABSOLUTELY FUN!

PASSION!

It is not the best outlet for your creative expression LET IT GO!

CREATIVE EXPRESSION puts you in a state of JOY

FEAR not GOOD enough, UNIQUE enough, NOVEL enough

24

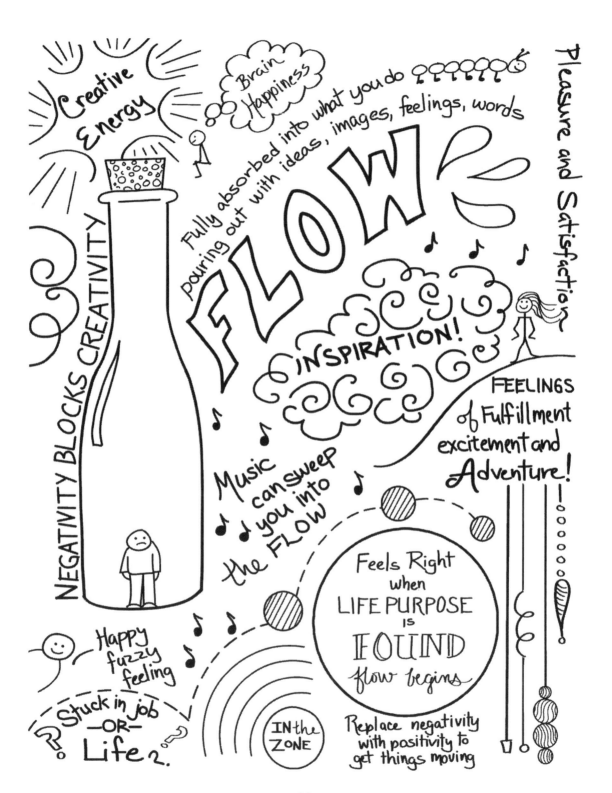

CHAPTER 2
Things to Improve On

These are key foundational skills, the building blocks to a great castle. Examining our weak links indicates where we are lacking and where we can improve. This involves a conversation with ourselves: Are my skills adequate? Can I do better?

Improvement

Patience

the capacity to accept or tolerate delay, trouble, or suffering without getting angry or upset.

INSTANT GRATIFICATION

IMPATIENCE
doesn't get others to move faster!

IMPATIENT PEOPLE
ARE PERCEIVED as:
- ✓ arrogant
- ✓ insensitive
- ✓ impulsive
- ✓ poor decision makers
- ✓ quick judgments
- ✓ interrupt
- ✓ poor people skills
- ✓ irritable
- ✓ tense
- ✓ anxious
- ✓ frustrated

PATIENCE takes PRACTICE!

Perfection DERAILS

BODY CHECK
- hunger
- dehydrated
- fatigue

IMPATIENCE RAISES OUR STRESS LEVELS DAMAGES RELATIONSHIPS

A-HA!

Journal WHY you are impatient

Become More AWARE

Journaling uncovers patterns and exposes triggers: events, people, or circumstances to uncover CAUSE

Imagine POSITIVE future outcomes!

PATIENCE [has] a magical effect... which DIFFICULTIES and obstacles disappear

VANISH!

RELAX

DEEP BREATH

SELF-TALK YOUR WAY OUT OF DOWNWARD

SPEAK SLOWLY, MOVE SLOWLY, BY ACTING MORE PATIENT YOU FEEL PATIENT

WHY ARE YOU IN SUCH A HURRY?

MAYBE YOUR TO DO LIST IS TOO LONG

......TAKE A BREAK OR WALK

— John Quincy Adams

Draw • Write • Get it onto Paper

LONG-TERM Patience

"Have patience with all things But first of all, with yourself."
—ST FRANCIS de SALES

Patience is A FORM OF ACTION
—Augusta Rodin

Frequent small CELEBRATIONS are a way to REWARD PATIENCE

ALL THINGS are Difficult before they BECOME EASY

ANSWERS COME TO YOU WHEN YOU LEAST expect it!

GRATITUDE Journal write 3 things you are THANKFUL for EVERY DAY!

Everything comes to you in the Right Moment

A moment of patience in a moment of anger saves a THOUSAND moments of REGRET
—Ali ibn Abu Talib

GRATITUDE REWIRES YOUR BRAIN to be OPTIMISTIC and strengthens PATIENCE

DELAYED success gives you a chance to Develop Skills AND Experience

Create a timeline to create VISION

Reflect, Meditate PRAY: PLAN

Adjust your dream

OPEN your mind to NEW Possibilities

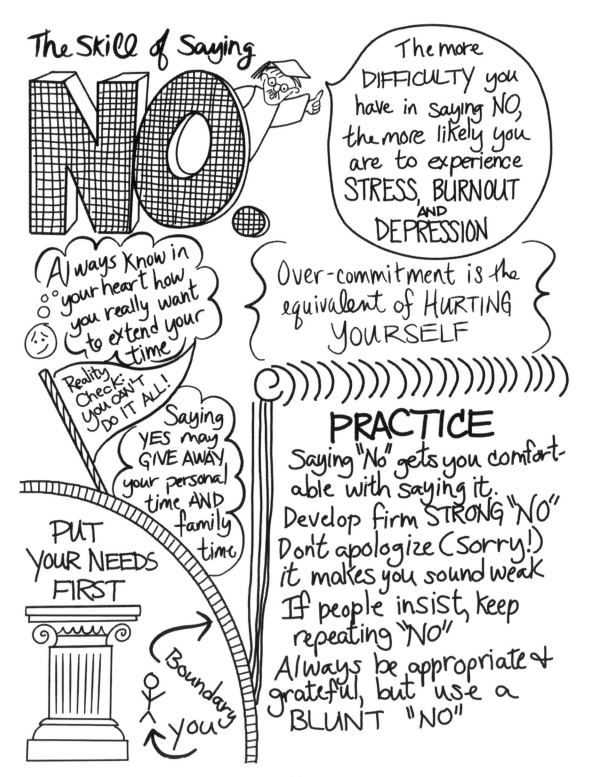

GOOD JUDGMENT
protects you from TOXIC RELATIONSHIPS

We feel something is not quite right.

Making decisions, drawing conclusions, is a PRIMAL INSTINCT for survival

We may feel threatened/defensive...

Others decisions seem illogical

Accepting REALITY can be a long JOURNEY

HMM...

Others decisions are harmful/hurtful

NAMING Poor behavior releases POWER the negative person has on US.

NAMING negative disorder can be a relief that BLAME does not lie with US

EVALUATION alerts us to put healthy boundaries in place

LABELS help us to sort information

LISTEN TO YOUR GUT

If we can NAME negative behavior, we can make informed action to deflect the negativity

QUIET

SILENCE IS A COMMUNICATION SKILL

silence has a way of making you look profound

NOT EVERYTHING that enters your MIND needs to exit your MOUTH

SILENCE is not meant to be filled

LISTEN MORE THAN SPEAK

3 and 3 check Allow others THREE FULL sentences in three minutes!

ASK OTHER PERSON QUESTIONS

BE a FLOWER and just enjoy the AIR
—RORI RAYE

SHORTEN YOUR QUESTIONS

FIGHT the URGE to FIX, to HELP, clarify —AND— EXPLAIN

CHOOSE to keep at least 1 OPINION to yourself EACH DAY.

STAND BACK... let others make their own mistakes —AND— Find their way

If you swear and use vulgar language ALL THE TIME, how will anyone know any difference when a ROCK falls on your Foot?

Profanity is for the UNINSPIRED!

UGLY WORDS out of a Beautiful FACE leaves NO BEAUTY

BE SURE to Taste your Words BEFORE YOU SPIT THEM OUT

GROW Vocabulary

Vulgarity IS NO SUBSTITUTE FOR WIT
—DOWAGER, DOWNTON ABBEY

If you CAN'T BE INTERESTING without profanity— you're not that INTERESTING

CREATIVE —and— Intelligent MINDS cannot exhaust BRILLANT·EXPRESSIVE COMMUNICATION

Use Language to Build + UPLIFT those AROUND you
—Thomas A. Monson

Always wear your INVISIBLE CROWN

58

The **SOUND** your *VOICE* makes indicates

A SMILE makes you SOUND more Pleasant

- Stress levels
- Mood
- Intentions

PRACTIICE matching the TONE of a KIND person you are talking with.

EXAGGERATE a SIMPLE SENTENCE "What do you want me to do?"

If your voice carries nothing but BURDEN - FRUSTRATION Listeners will soon TIRE of YOU.

EMPHASIZE different words: Say with ANGER COMPASSION CONFUSION

THANK you. I am SO GRATEFUL!

Record your voice, telling your story, your burden. Play it back to yourself.

Repeat 1 comment about yourself until you can deliver it free of emotional unpleasantries.

TRAIN your EAR to hear the NEGATIVE VIBE.

Do You Speak FLUENT SARCASM?

ARE you the SOURCE of OTHER'S HURT? ARE you a daily, hourly, constant offender? You CAN DO BETTER!

Hostile Sarcasm DEVALUES People

When you're HAPPIER it's so much easier to be nice to those around you!

HURT   UNKIND   BULLY   DAMAGING

ITS REALLY, REALLY, REALLY, REALLY HARD TO STOP BEING SARCASTIC!

DO:

1. Observe others who have a kind way with words.
2. Tell somebody you are trying to stop-accountability is priceless.
3. Tally yourself to get a REAL perspective on frequent abuse.
4. Spend time thinking how you want to use your words and how you don't.
5. Make your positive defense mechanism LAUGHTER.
6. Sarcasm reinforces negative thinking FIND HAPPIER THOUGHTS.
7. Misery loves company-avoid SARCASM ADDICTS.

CHANGE doesn't happen BY ACCIDENT

25¢ SARCASTIC REMARK

CHAPTER 3
Get a Better Attitude

Here's where a little trickle turns into a dangerous flood. Focusing and binging on negativity and self-pity is a dire pastime. The pictures we paint hold no sunshine. It's a time to start painting a new, better picture of brighter possibilities.

Positivity

Draw • Write • Get it onto Paper

—OUR BRAIN HAS—
50,000 thoughts a day!

Carry Positive WORDS with you every DAY!

Healthy self-talk is a ratio of 2 positive thoughts for every NEGATIVE thought

POSITIVE	NEGATIVE
upbeat-uplifting	destructive
self-validating	miserable
factual	critical
supportive	harsh
	magnified
	out of perspective

INNER **VOICE** . . . Give "it" a name

"BIG MEANIE"
The "NAG"
Silly or Goofy name

Are YOU BINGING on NEGATIVITY ?

GET RID OF YOUR NEGATIVE BUDDIES
people who feed on drama and misery love to hear about yours

"Some buddies sucked me IN SO QUICKLY I didn't even NOTICE until I walked away completely DRENCHED in DAMAGING FEELINGS"
—Anonymous

GET A POSITIVE, SUPPORTIVE FRIEND

YES ...I AM talking to myself and it's a PRIVATE conversation!

The answer to feeling POOR inside is to gather some RICHES... a person who is rich inside feels as if she has ENOUGH. She is STRONG enough and GOOD enough. She takes responsibility for EVERY VICTORY and every failure.
— DEEPAK CHOPRA

Self-pity is a slippery slope leading to an ugly habit OR launching us to change our situation for the better.

complain, entitled, wallow, mope, victim, stuck, poor me crave sympathy, dwell on the past, self-sabotage, poor me impede progress, avoid taking responsibility, poor me

Help Others

AVOID SYMPATHIZING TOO MUCH • LISTEN • OFFER REASSURANCE • BRAINSTORM SOLUTIONS ...in the end it's up to them to change

CHAPTER 4
Accept Myself

We are our own worst critic, holding ourselves to impossible standards with no acknowledgment of victory. We hold ourselves back from all the wonderful things life has in store for us.

Spend some time thinking about how much power you give to these perceived defects and shortcomings. Most of all, learn to be kind to yourself.

Acceptance

Motivation Killing
Killing
PERFECTION

FEAR of FAILURE
is a
POWERFUL
MOTIVATION TO
NEVER
make an
ATTEMPT
FEAR of
SUCCESS
SQUASH PLAYFULLY!

1. Does it really matter in the big scheme of things?
2. Will it matter tomorrow, next week, next year?
3. Can I survive the worst that will happen?
4. Allow yourself to make mistakes.
5. Begin projects with a "good enough" plan.
6. Amazing doesn't happen right away.
7. Shave back number of hours you spend on a project.
8. Be OK not to be praised (praise yourself)!

Draw · Write · Get it onto paper

PERFECT

The Perfectionist

- Overly thorough
- Unappreciated
- Anger
- Unhappy
- Anxiety
- Procrastination
- Depression
- Avoid Risks
- Overly cautious
- Unrealistic goals
- Exhausted
- Give up easily
- poor coping skills
- criticize self HARSHLY
- Indecisive
- Avoid trying NEW things
- Feelings of NOT capable
- Frustrated
- self-worth based on accomplish-ment
- Mistakes seen as personal defects
- Avoiding situations
- LOW self-esteem
- Fear others will only like "perfect" them
- Side tracked by little things
- get bogged down in details
- Scared of making mistakes
- "Should" statements
- Disappointed with self
- Don't ask for help
- All or nothing attitude
- Constantly trying to improve things
- Achievement is temporary
- Rely on praise of others
- Fear of failure

The Little Voice in Our Heads...

1. STOP! Say a powerful STOP! out loud to negative thoughts.

2. SNAP a rubber band on your wrist to ZAP negative self-talk.

3. Put hand over mouth to block negative WORDS.

4. YOU — Talk to yourself in terms of you: "You look GREAT in this outfit!"

5. RE-FRAME: It's raining I can't wait to enjoy the new flowers!

6. SURROUND yourself with POSITIVE PEOPLE! I ♥ MONDAYS!

7. VISUALIZE a TINY box and put negativity in it to minimize.

8. STATE the FACTS: "I am NOT as big as a whale."

9. TALK to inner-voice like a CHILD: "Behave yourself!"

10. NEGATIVITY DETOX PUSH the POSITIVE 1 week 1 month OR 1 area of your LIFE.

11. SUPPORT YOURSELF Like supporting a friend: "Joe, you've Got THIS!"

"The more you TALK YOURSELF DOWN, SECOND-GUESS yourself, and see changes as CALAMITOUS, the LESS FREE your mind will be to roam through CREATIVE SOLUTIONS of the problems you face." —Rogelberg Study

114

CHAPTER 5
Seek a New Perspective

There truly are outside factors beyond our control that make us feel helpless. Burdens, depression and circumstances we view as unfair weigh us down. It can be hard to reach a higher vantage point that will allow us fresh air and a clearer picture.

Working through struggles has the potential for healing. Slowly, we become better and can see things more clearly. We then can become healers to those around us, showing patience, understanding, and empathy.

Perspective

JUDGING

LIFE'S NOT FAIR!

Sometimes we need to accept what's unfair

VICTIMIZE SELF to avoid responsibility

BLAME OTHERS (chip on shoulders)

CONSTANT BITTERNESS & GRUMBLING

NO ONE UNDERSTANDS MY LIFE they've got it **EASY**

This is a form of judging AND bitterness of INJUSTICE

UNFAIRNESS triggers the part of the brain that controls FEAR + ANGER = Anxiety

◆ Catch emotional response BEFORE it leads to obsessive thinking
◆ Think RATIONALLY before acting
◆ Recognize difference between what you can and cannot CONTROL

We don't think rationally or respond positively

In reality, everyone at some point has TRIALS in their LIFE

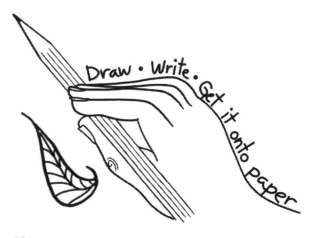

Draw • Write • Get it onto Paper

BURDENS

It's not the HEAVY LOAD that BREAKS you, its the WAY you carry it.
—Lou Holtz

BURDENS can push you into a NEGATIVITY PIT

1. People are unaware of what I am going through

Sometimes when I say "I'm OK" I need someone to look me in the eyes, hug me tight and say "I know you are not."

I can't be happy for people when they are happy. I don't know why I expect them to mind-read my unhappiness. They can't possibly know every detail of my life — but I expect them to.

2. Tell other people so that your burden can be lightened or shared.

My sarcastic remarks and tone are REALLY trying to tell you I am spread too thin, LIFE is TOO BIG for me right now am I am overwhelmed with the weight of it ALL

3. Keep a GRATITUDE JOURNAL

You deserve KINDNESS + GENTLENESS from yourself!

BURNOUT is a state of emotional, mental, + physical exhaustion caused by excessive + prolonged STRESS

BURNOUT CAN be HEALED

SOMETIMES LIFE IS TOO BIG...

you feel overwhelmed, tired, ANGRY

BURNOUT... and a pit of... NOTHINGNESS and DESPAIR

* Anyone who feels overworked and undervalued is at risk for BURNOUT.

ROAD to BURNOUT:
- Every day is a bad day
- Exhausted all the time
- Get sick more easily
- Feel helpless, negative
- Lack motivation
- No control over life
- Procrastinate, failure
- Stretched too thin
- No time for relaxing or socializing
- Not supported
- Lack of sleep

" If excessive stress is like drowning in responsibilities, burnout is being ALL DRIED-UP "

128

GET OUT of your HEAD and start interacting with PEOPLE... to maintain PERSPECTIVE.
—Joe Serio

FEELING WHAT I AM GOING THROUGH!

[Everyone's] purse holds JUNK Secret Pain and Dissatisfaction
—COURTNEY JOSEPH

NO ONE UNDERSTANDS

Talk to a FRIEND

Find a POWERFUL LISTENER

Feeling UNDERSTOOD IS THE Most INCREDIBLE feeling in the WORLD

We ALL have COMMON struggles, but our PUZZLES are all DIFFERENT
—COURTNEY JOSEPH

SUPPORT GROUP

When you feel someone isn't listening to you, listen to THEM First

CHAPTER 6
Rise Above Ugly

Difficult people shuffle into and out of our lives, quietly (or loudly) wreaking havoc. Sometimes they are with us for the long haul. Many of us may not even realize the cloud that has drifted in from a toxic person.

Awareness is critical. Being hurt is an injury we must tend to. We must understand how forgiveness works and preserve ourselves in the process.

Protect

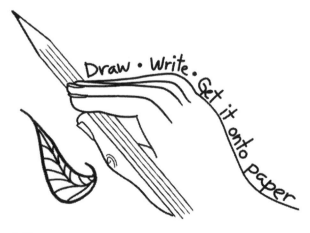

Draw · Write · Get it onto Paper

143

Attracting Toxic People?

you are:
great listener
generous with time
open and honest
easy going
peace keeper
sunny disposition
Positive

Setting boundaries takes courage and conviction — it's the greatest LOVE we can show ourselves and build the life we deserve

you might be an EASY TARGET

You are a BRILLANT STAR, WORTHY of

Saying No can be the ULTIMATE self-care

Safe - Guarding

FORGIVENESS is a gift to yourself... because You Deserve Peace

Forgiveness changes the FUTURE

I want to forgive BUT right now, I'm not ready

WHY

FOR-GIVENESS is a PROCESS

It takes time

Did they HURT me?

INTENTIONAL
Immature
Accident
THREATENED

Bad Judgment
FEAR of Loss
MENTAL ILLNESS
Not Good Enough

Jealousy

MENTAL PHYSICAL
Benefits of Forgiveness

☐ healthier relationships
☐ sense of well-being
☐ less anxiety, stress, and hostility
☐ lower blood pressure
☐ fewer symptoms of depression
☐ strong immune system
☐ improved heart health
☐ higher self-esteem

— MAYO CLINIC

STOP!

Forgiveness is NOT:
— giving in
— letting the offender off the hook
— reconciling
— having to socialize OR like them

Allow Space
for the fullness of the events to unfold in your // MIND

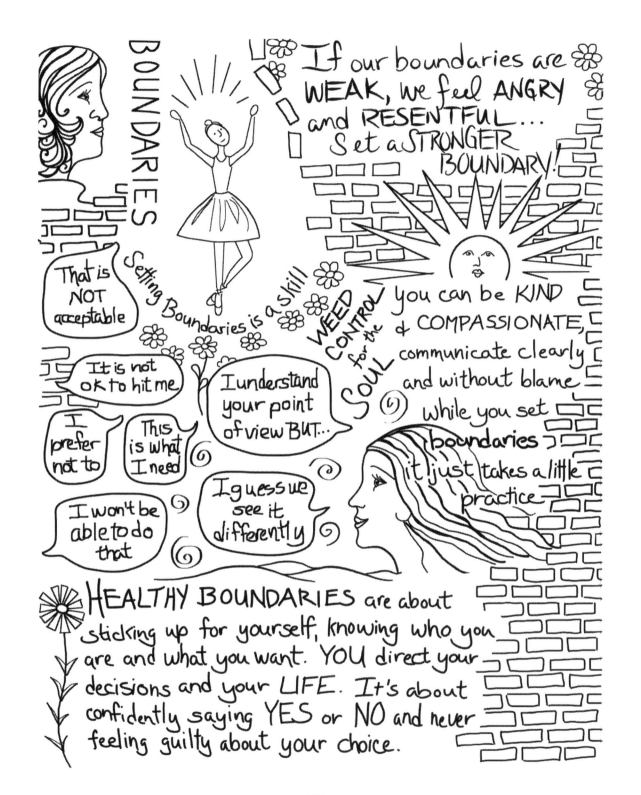

BOUNDARIES

If our boundaries are WEAK, we feel ANGRY and RESENTFUL... Set a STRONGER BOUNDARY!

Setting Boundaries is a skill

That is NOT acceptable

It is not ok to hit me

I prefer not to

This is what I need

I understand your point of view BUT...

I won't be able to do that

I guess ue see it differently

WEED CONTROL for the SOUL

you can be KIND & COMPASSIONATE, communicate clearly and without blame while you set boundaries it just takes a little practice

HEALTHY BOUNDARIES are about sticking up for yourself, knowing who you are and what you want. YOU direct your decisions and your LIFE. It's about confidently saying YES or NO and never feeling guilty about your choice.

154

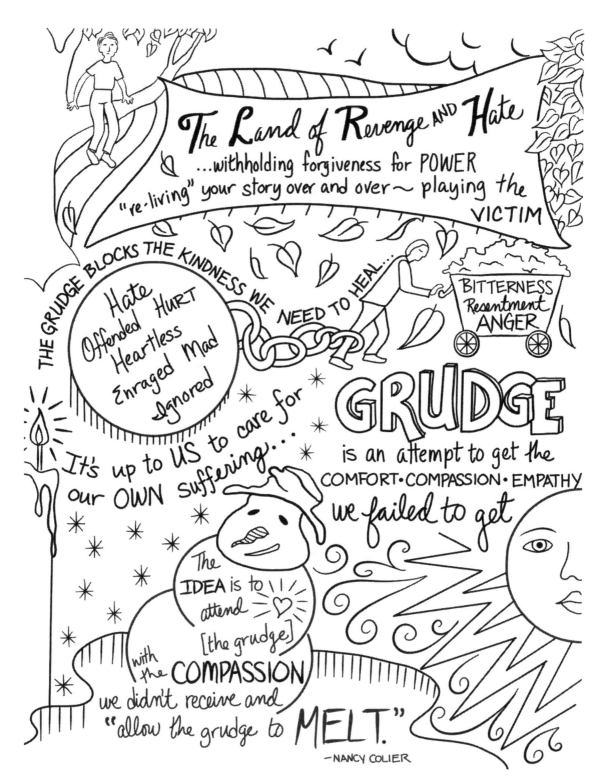

The Land of Revenge AND Hate

...withholding forgiveness for POWER

"re-living" your story over and over ~ playing the VICTIM

THE GRUDGE BLOCKS THE KINDNESS WE NEED TO HEAL...

Hate Hurt Offended Heartless Enraged Mad Ignored

BITTERNESS Resentment ANGER

GRUDGE

is an attempt to get the COMFORT · COMPASSION · EMPATHY we failed to get

It's up to US to care for our OWN suffering...

The IDEA is to attend [the grudge] with the COMPASSION we didn't receive and "allow the grudge to MELT."

—NANCY COLIER

We can only be ANGRY · OFFENDED · JUDGMENTAL of OTHERS when we are afraid of the same thing · IN US ·

Our Reaction reveals OUR feelings of strength or inadequacy

Look for the positive AVOID stereotyping

connection to identify with others

Judging bonds us to people whom we want to accept us

Focus on finding a shared

insecure · scared · lonely

Judging

When we stop judging others, we find the FREEDOM to STOP JUDGING ourselves

when...

OUR INFO ON OTHERS only adds up to a GRAIN of SAND

· Hurts people
· Perpetuates stereotypes
· Makes you feel worse about yourself
· Adds negativity/hatred into the world
· Encourages you to judge yourself

Monitor your thoughts
Focus on your OWN LIFE
Remember how judging FEELS

Looking for the BEST in others is EASIER when you feel the BEST about YOURSELF

CHAPTER 7
Me Time

There's no one who can heal us like ourselves. Allowing important time for self-care is the first step into putting us back on a path to the happy, emotionally balanced beings we were made to be.

Are you taking care of yourself? Do you allow yourself all the time you deserve? Reviving your spirit and mind is vital to your life spark. Enjoy a happy heart through exploring, self-reflection, and personal care.

Reflect

I am Too AMAZING TO BE A DOORMAT

OR I Don't Do Guilt

WE ARE CONFUSED WHEN PEOPLE WE LOVE MAKE US feel

✓ Not loved
✓ Not valued
✓ Worthless
✓ Shame
✓ Controlled
✓ Lied to
✓ Manipulated
✓ Ignored
✓ Inadequate

WARNING! causes MASSIVE STRESS Response

TOXIC WASTE

IN OUR LIFE

◆ Narcissist/Codependent
◆ Emotional Vampires
◆ Control Freaks
◆ Bully/Cruel
◆ Gossiper, Liars
◆ Negative People

DANGER • DANGER • DANGER

Distance yourself—Beware irrational Behavior
Boundaries mean NOTHING!

Draw · Write · Get it onto paper

No one else can heal you the way you heal yourself. That is your own special MAGIC.
—PAVANA

Chocolate · Tea of choice

Self Care

· Essential oils · relaxing music · create · meditate · breathe · spa · exercise ·

FIND HAPPINESS

Look for meaning & satisfaction in family, friends, or hobby

rest · journal · take time off · laugh · dream · play

Make choices that keep you ENERGIZED Inspired and FULFILLED

Be KIND to yourself

When you're HAPPY, problems don't seem so BIG and you think more CREATIVELY

IMMERSE in Positivity

Nourish your Creative Side

pray · yoga · visualize

FIND VALUE in what you do...

Ahhhhh

172

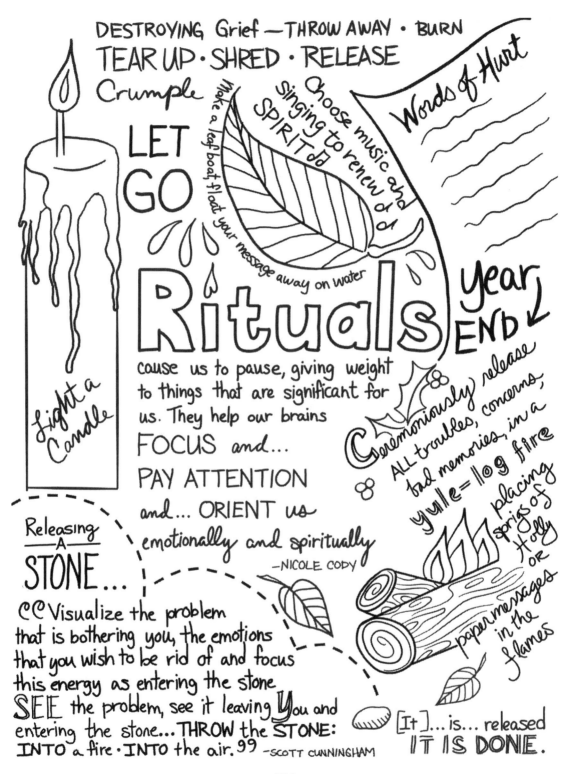

DESTROYING Grief —THROW AWAY • BURN
TEAR UP • SHRED • RELEASE
Crumple

Make a leaf boat float your message away on water

Choose music and singing to renew of SPIRIT ♪♫

Words of Hurt

LET GO

Light a Candle

Rituals

YEAR END

cause us to pause, giving weight to things that are significant for us. They help our brains FOCUS and...
PAY ATTENTION and... ORIENT us emotionally and spiritually
—NICOLE CODY

Ceremoniously release ALL troubles, concerns, bad memories, in a yulle=llog fire placing sprigs of Holly OR paper messages in the flames

Releasing A STONE...

"Visualize the problem that is bothering you, the emotions that you wish to be rid of and focus this energy as entering the stone. SEE the problem, see it leaving You and entering the stone... THROW the STONE: INTO a fire • INTO the air." —SCOTT CUNNINGHAM

[It]...is...released
IT IS DONE.

176

NEW LIST
- New hopes
- New dreams

GO TO THE WOODS, or a private place where you can be undisturbed. DIG A HOLE in the ground near a tree or bush. POUR ALL OF YOUR *feelings* INTO THAT HOLE.

When done, cover the hole and thank the tree for LISTENING. Thank [the] Earth for RECEIVING. your Grief.

My nose prickles. My throat stings. My chest is tight. SADNESS and HURT flow through me.

"I RELEASE my pain, it is DONE"

Draw • Write • Get it onto paper...

let down • pain • lost opportunities • suffering • failure • rejection • loss • insults • Outcast • Anger • Despair • Frustration • disappointment • HURT

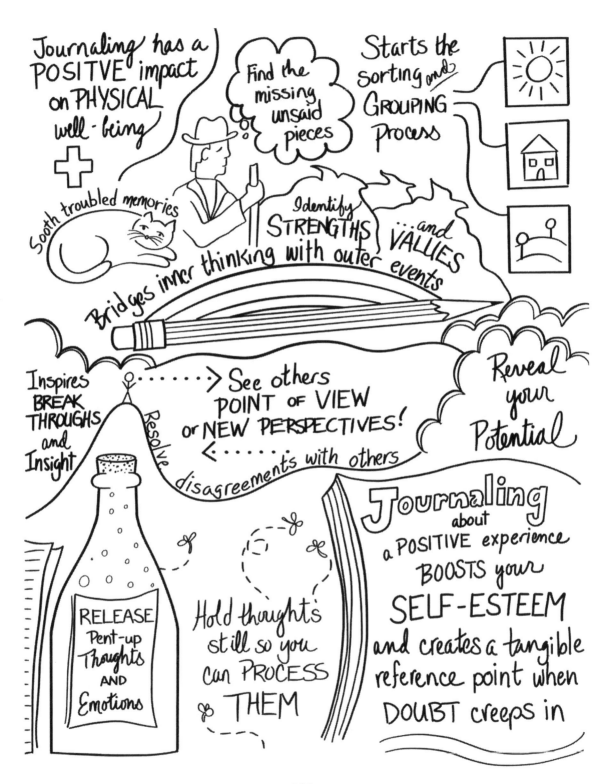

CHAPTER 8
Goals and Finish Lines

Nothing happens as fast as we would like it. Change, success, and personal victories all take time. Sometimes we must visualize a different ending to our story. Either way, deep within us is the driving force and determination to reach our goals. That's why it's important to invest time in yourself in ways that will help you focus and bring clarity to your path.

Finally, your time is coming. Celebrate your achievements, even the small ones - you're worth it.

I CAN DO IT!

Draw • Write • Get it onto paper

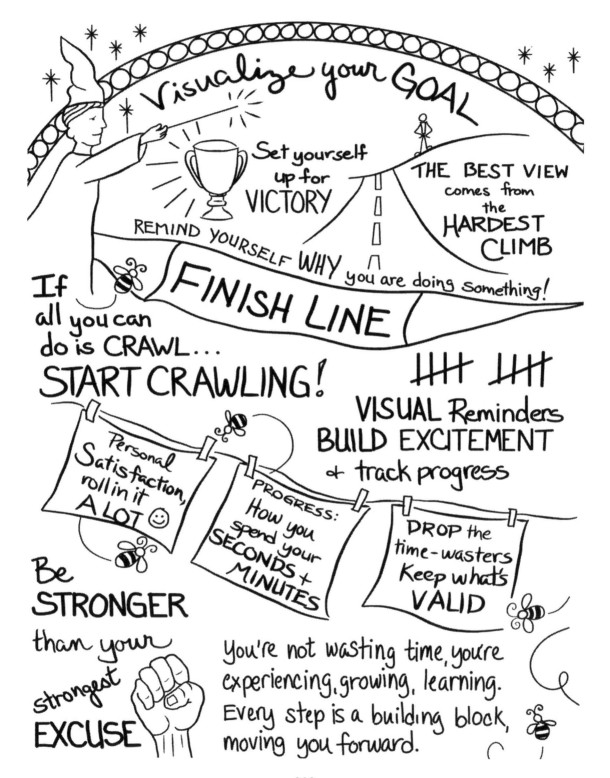

Visualize your GOAL

Set yourself up for VICTORY

THE BEST VIEW comes from the HARDEST CLIMB

REMIND YOURSELF WHY you are doing something!

FINISH LINE

If all you can do is CRAWL... START CRAWLING!

VISUAL Reminders BUILD EXCITEMENT + track progress

Personal Satisfaction, roll in it A LOT ☺

PROGRESS: How you spend your SECONDS + MINUTES

DROP the time-wasters Keep what's VALID

Be STRONGER than your strongest EXCUSE

You're not wasting time, you're experiencing, growing, learning. Every step is a building block, moving you forward.

ABOUT THE AUTHOR/ARTIST

Renee Matt considers herself to be a "multipod," a talented and curious person with many passions. She's managed to take each unique and fabulous facet of herself and roll it into Mattie-Moon.com. It's her playground where she gets to ponder, write, and doodle to her heart's content, and where she indulges her comic-persona Mattie Moon.

To learn more about multi-passionate/multi-potential/scanners, creatively-wired brains, or get a closer look at the inspiration, methods, and tools used for this book, visit **Mattie-Moon.com**. Look for Renee's fun designs that celebrate amazing, creative minds at **100-Passions.com**.

A WORD ABOUT FONTS AND SYMBOLS

Fonts are fun, they can strike a mood and add just the right touch to any project. For my book title, I selected the font "Against Myself" by Christopher Hanson. I loved the sketchiness of it with hints of doodling. I really liked it, but I thought the symbols might be interpreted the wrong way.

The designer uses two symbols, the anarchist symbol ("A" inside a circle) and the international squatter's symbol (kraakteken), a circle with a lightning-shaped arrow running upwards to the right. Both symbols have political ties along with different meanings varying by country.

In a positive light, the anarchist symbol is said to be a symbol of unity and determination, especially in oppressive conditions. The term "squatters" often applies to people with few resources, unable to obtain housing and who take up residence at a place without having legal claim. Squatting has resulted in positive outcomes, with participants shining light on social issues that need changing.

It's very clever of the designer to work in symbols that often represent conflict and then name the font "Against Myself." It seemed even more appropriate to use the font for a book on self-reflection and art journaling. I hope you have enjoyed the visual journey I have provided and added your own meaningful marks and thoughts along the way.

WHAT DID YOU THINK?

THANK YOU for taking the time to experience "Journal Juice: Everyday Life Topics for Journal Writing, Drawing, Dreaming, and Doodling." I am excited that you discovered this book and decided to give it a try!

What was your favorite page? Did a certain topic "speak" to you? Were you inspired to doodle, color, or create? Is there something you wished I would have included? Or maybe you bought it as a gift for someone? I would LOVE to hear your feedback!

Visit my website and drop me a comment, or leave feedback on the site where you purchased the book… can't wait to hear from you!

- Renee Matt AKA "Mattie Moon"

WORKS CITED

Adams, John Quincy. BrainyQuote.com. Explore Inc, 2016. 20 December 2016. www.brainyquote.com/quotes/quotes/j/johnquincy387094.html.

De Sales, St. Francis. "Top 25 Quotes of Saint Francis De Sales" (of 201)." *A-Z Quotes*. A-Z Quotes, n.d. Web. 20 Dec. 2016. www.azquotes.com/author/12905-Saint_Francis_de_Sales.

Deschene, Lori. "How to Deal with Unfairness and Change the Things You Can." *Tiny Buddha*. Tiny Buddha, 10 Nov. 2016. Web. 19 Dec. 2016. tinybuddha.com/blog/how-to-deal-with-unfairness-and-change-the-things-you-can/.

Eliot, George. BrainyQuote.com. Xplore Inc, 2016. 19 December 2016. www.brainyquote.com/quotes/quotes/g/georgeelio161679.html.

Biali, Dr. Susan. "Don't Try to Reason with Unreasonable People." *Dr. Susan Biali*. Dr. Susan Biali, 21 Jan. 2012. Web. 19 Dec. 2016. susanbiali.com/dont-try-to-reason-with-unreasonable-people/.

Burroughs, John. BrainyQuote.com. Xplore Inc, 20119 6. December 2016. Web. www.brainyquote.com/quotes/quotes/j/johnburrou121353.html.

Cameron, Tim. *The Forty-Day Word Fast: A Spiritual Journey to Eliminate Toxic Words From Your Life*. N.p.: Charisma House, 2015. Print.

Catherine the Great. BrainyQuote.com. Xplore Inc, 2016. 19 December 2016. www.brainyquote.com/quotes/quotes/c/catherinet108926.html.

Chopra, Deepak. "Ask Deepak: How to Stop Feeling Self-Pity." *Oprah.com*. Oprah.com, n.d. Web. 20 Dec. 2016. www.oprah.com/spirit/How-to-Stop-Feeling-Self-Pity-Ask-Deepak.

Cody, Nicole. "Burning the Past – A Ritual for Cleansing Pain." *Cauldrons and Cupcakes*. Nicole Cody, 24 Oct. 2012. Web. 20 Dec. 2016. cauldronsandcupcakes.com/2012/10/24/burning-the-past-a-ritual-for-cleansing-pain/.

Cohen, Leonard. BrainyQuote.com. Xplore Inc, 2016. 20 December 2016. www.brainyquote.com/quotes/quotes/l/leonardcoh156369.html.

Colier, Nancy. "Why We Hold Grudges, and How to Let Them Go." *Psychology Today*. Psychology Today, 4 Mar. 2015. Web. 19 Dec. 2016. www.psychologytoday.com/blog/inviting-monkey-tea/201503/why-we-hold-grudges-and-how-let-them-go.

Dark, Alvin. BrainyQuote.com. Xplore Inc, 2016. 20 December 2016. www.brainyquote.com/quotes/quotes/a/alvindark139404.html.

Gaiman, Neil. BrainyQuote.com. Xplore Inc, 2016. 20 December 2016. www.brainyquote.com/quotes/quotes/n/neilgaiman461447.html.

Holtz, Lou. BrainyQuote.com. Xplore Inc, 2016. 19 December 2016. www.brainyquote.com/quotes/quotes/l/louholtz120090.html.

Hudson, Paul. "6 Failures You Should Experience If You Want To Succeed In Life." *Elite Daily*. Elite Daily, 06 Aug. 2015. Web. 19 Dec. 2016. elitedaily.com/life/motivation/failures-to-make-want-succeed-in-life/922082/.

Joseph, Courtney. "When It Feels Like No One Understands." *Women Living Well*. Women Living Well, 10 Mar. 2015. Web. 21 Dec. 2016. womenlivingwell.org/2013/03/when-it-feels-like-no-one-understands/.

Mackay, Harvey. "Obey the 24-hour Rule." *Washington Examiner*. The Washington Examiner Http://www.washingtonexaminer.com/s3/wex15/img/wex_eagle_large.png, 19 Mar. 2012. Web. 19 Dec. 2016. www.washingtonexaminer.com/obey-the-24-hour-rule/article/111605. In reference to the philosophy of Miami Dolphins coach, Don Shula.

Mayo Clinic Staff. "Adult Health." *Forgiveness: Letting Go of Grudges and Bitterness - Mayo Clinic*. Mayo Clinic, 11 Nov. 2014. Web. 26 Dec. 2016. www.mayoclinic.org/healthy-lifestyle/adult-health/in-depth/forgiveness/art-20047692.

McLeod, Lisa Earle. "The Shower Speech You Might Want to Shelve." *Mcleodandmore.com*. Lisa Earle McLeod, 22 Oct. 2009. Web. 19 Dec. 2016.

www.mcleodandmore.com/2009/10/22/the-shower-speech-you-might-want-to-shelve/.

Nietzsche, Friedrich. BrainyQuote.com. Xplore Inc, 2016. 21 December 2016. www.brainyquote.com/quotes/quotes/f/friedrichn162010.html.

Nightingale, Earl. BrainyQuote.com. Xplore Inc, 2016. 19 December 2016. www.brainyquote.com/quotes/quotes/e/earlnighti107070.html.

Oppong, Thomas. "Get Out of Your Comfort Zone (Your Success Depends on It)." Blog post. *All Top Start Ups*. Thomas Oppong, 24 July 2014. Web. alltopstartups.com/2014/07/24/get-out-of-your-comfort-zone/.

Pavana. "Images by Mazadohta." *Imgrum*. Pavana, n.d. Web. 20 Dec. 2016. www.imgrum.net/user/mazadohta/1918283879/1254471191305691452_1918283879

Raye, Rori. "When You Want To Explain – Teach Yourself To Keep Your Mouth Shut Instead."*Have the Relationship You Want*. Rori Raye, n.d. Web. 20 Dec. 2016. blog.havetherelationshipyouwant.com/love-life/when-you-want-to-explain-teach-yourself-to-keep-your-mouth-shut-instead/.

Rodin, Auguste. Artnet.com. Artnet Worldwide Corp, 2016. 20 December 2016. news.artnet.com/art-world/auguste-rodin-birthday-quotes-745238.

Ryan, Liz. "Ten Signs Your Job Doesn't Deserve You." *Linked In*. Linked In, 5 Aug. 2013. Web. 20 Dec. 2016. www.linkedin.com/pulse/20130805121451-52594-ten-signs-your-job-doesn-t-deserve-you.

Schuller, Robert H. BrainyQuote.com. Xplore Inc, 2016. 19 December 2016. www.brainyquote.com/quotes/quotes/r/roberthsc120987.html.

Serio, Joe. "Do You Feel like No One Understands What You're Going Through?" *Joe Serio*. Joe Serio, 07 Sept. 2014. Web. 25 Dec. 2016. joeserio.com/do-you-feel-like-no-one-understands-what-youre-going-through/.

Talib, Ali Ibn Abu. "Ali Ibn Abi Talib Quote:." Quote Fancy. Quote Fancy, n.d. Web. 20 Dec. 2016. quotefancy.com/quote/1439325/Ali-ibn-Abi-Talib-A-moment-of-patience-in-a-moment-of-anger-prevents-a-thousand-moments.

Tubman, Harriet. BrainyQuote.com. Xplore Inc, 2016. 19 December 2016.
www.brainyquote.com/quotes/quotes/h/harriettub310306.html.

Whitbourne Ph.D., Susan Krauss. "Make Your Self-Talk Work for You." *Psychology Today*. Psychology Today, n.d. Web. 26 Dec. 2016.
www.psychologytoday.com/blog/fulfillment-any-age/201309/make-your-self-talk-work-you. In reference to the Rogelberg study.